Dedication:

To All Children of the World

ISBN 0-913678-23-6

First Printing
Copyright © 1992 by New Day Press, Inc.

Love is a Child

New Day Press, Inc.

Karamu House
2355 East 89th St.
Cleveland, Ohio 44104

Love is a Child

Written by
Kenyette Adrine-Robinson

Illustrated by
Gayle Audrell Sanders

<u>Love is a Child</u> is a book of many faces with many stereotypical labels. What the author is trying to do is destroy the misconceptions about children's feelings while exposing some of the falsehoods put upon the little ones.

The children are our future which means that we need to establish good communications filled with love and with respect. This book deals with interpersonal communications: child to parent, child to teacher, and adult to child.

The author and illustrator hope that the readers of <u>Love is a Child</u>, can and will, feel compassion for the children as they explore these passages.

Please read and enjoy.

Written by
Kenyette Adrine-Robinson

Illustrated by
Gayle Audrell Sanders

1

Say, we listen to many words and the word kids makes us wonder who we really are.

We are offsprings of Moms and Dads.

3

We come in all colors
red, yellow, black and white.

4

We're not crumb-snatchers;
however, we do take
cookies and fruit from
the table. (smile)

5

We are not
yard-apes, but
we do like
to play outside.

6

Kids spill things like milk, soup and juice on the rug, but we're still not rug rats.

Whatever happened to nice words like boys and girls, prince and princess?

8

We like being called young ladies and

9 young men.

We love to be known as Daddy's little
man or Daddy's little girl.

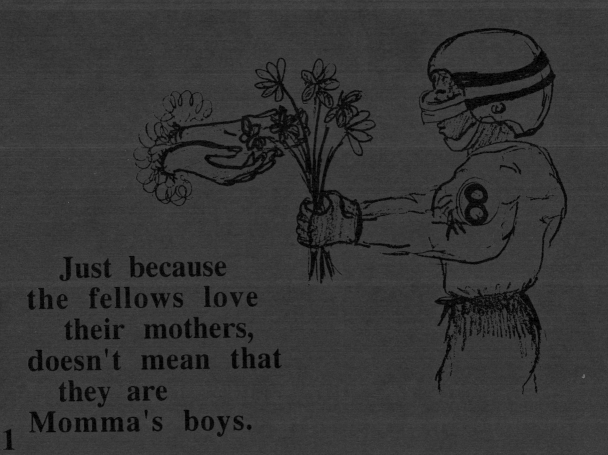

Just because
the fellows love
their mothers,
doesn't mean that
they are
Momma's boys.

11

Grown-ups spoil us with toys and sweet things to eat, but the greatest gift that you can give is the gift of love.

Smile at us wee ones, and
we'll smile back at you!

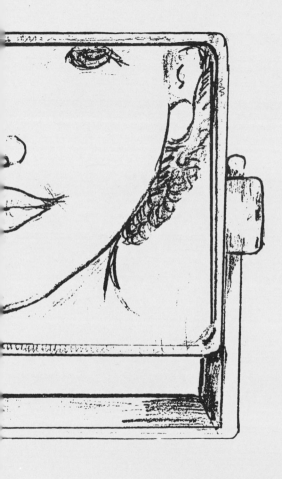

You need us
like we need you,
sharing love
through and
through.

As you take us back through your childhood, will you remember to teach us your history?

16

We need you to show us the way.

17

18

Help us to understand past generations.

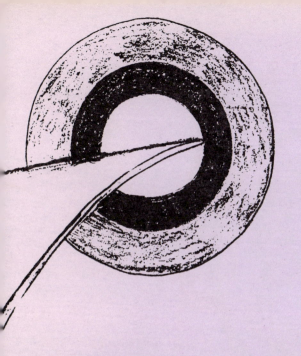

We are the future!

21   **Teach us about the earth's fruits.**

You may call us kids, but we still love YOU!

About the Author Kenyette Adrine-Robinson is a native Clevelander. Kenyette has a B.A. in Photo-Journalism-News with a minor in African American Affairs. She holds two Masters of Education. One in Student Personnel Administration in Higher Education. The other is in Special Education. She is currently teaching at Kent State University in the Department of Pan-African Studies, her alma mater.

Collections of her poetry are:

Thru Kenyette Eyes and Be My Shoo-gar. She is also the editor of Black Image Makers. Kenyette is also on the Board of Trustees for the Poets League of Greater Cleveland.

About the Illustrator. Gayle Audrell Sanders, an alumna of Northwestern University and Case Western Reserve University's Graduate School, is an assistant professor of English, Reading, and Speech at Harold Washington College in Chicago, Illinois. She has two sons, Damian Alexander and Darien Amiel. Her works-in-progress include a book of visionary poetry, a trilogy, and a series of children's books that offers hope to our people who are struggling to remain whole in the midst of poverty, violence and deprivation.

This Book Belongs To:

_____